ADA CHR Andrea DeYoung

3W

Library of Congress Catalog Card Number: 55-4742

Reprinted 1966

Distributed by: Ginn and Company: Boston
The Awani Press: Fresno, California

A Day With Tupi

An
authentic story
of an Indian boy
in California's mountains

by Fran Hubbard
illustrated by Ed Vella

TUPI, THE CHIPMUNK

★ ★

Many, many moons ago in the beautiful valley called A-wa-ni there lived a little Indian boy. His name was Tupi, which in the language of his people meant "chipmunk". One warm summer day Tupi lay on his back in the tall grass, daydreaming. High above him towered granite cliffs whose walls were dotted with giant trees. In these cliffs lived Lee-ka, the red-tailed hawk, who spent his days soaring high above the valley searching for food. In the tree over Tupi's head two gray squirrels chattered and scolded noisily as they chased each other 'round and 'round the branches. Tupi was the friend of all of the animals but his special friends were the chipmunks because from them he received his name.

Tupi was dreaming of the day when he would be older and could go with his father on the hunt. He would be the bravest of them all. He would bring food for the whole village for he would shoot the largest deer. His mother and father would be proud. His grandmother and grandfather would be proud. Just when he was dreaming of the feast the village would have in his honor, Tupi's dream was interrupted by the voice of his mother, and soon he found himself scuffing his way toward the stream, a pitch-covered water basket under his arm.

As he neared the water's edge the little Indian boy heard a splashing sound. Quietly he parted the willows. There stood Mo-ho, the black bear, in the shallow water, while her two little brown cubs rolled and played on the grassy bank.

The cubs had been born during the previous winter, while the mother was in her "winter sleep", and they had not seen the light of day until they were three months old. As the next winter approached they too would have to think of eating lots of food to build up fat, and they would have to look for a snug den in which to sleep while the snow was on the ground.

The mother bear was motionless, with one paw raised. As Tupi watched the paw flashed through the water and a silvery fish was flipped onto the ground near the cubs. Pushing and growling the the cubs pounced on the feast.

Tupi made his way quietly upstream. As he knelt by the water-fall the air was filled with a beautiful trilling song. It was his friend the dipper, whose mossy nest was behind the fall. Bobbing a friendly greeting the little gray bird dived into the stream. Tupi watched as the dipper walked on the bottom of the stream, gathering food for his family.

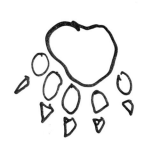

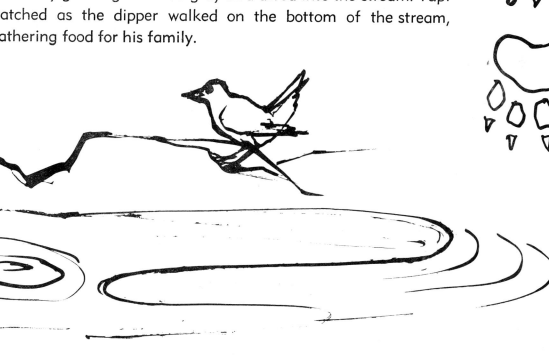

All of the birds and other animals living in the A-wa-ni were important, and Tupi knew what each did to help his people. There was the flicker, who gave his feathers for the headbands worn for certain dances. The top-knots of the valley quail and the red feathers of the acorn woodpeckers were used for decorations on the beautiful baskets woven by the Indian women. Feathers for arrows came from the red-tailed hawk and from Ui-uyu, the roadrunner. The Indians believed that Ui-uyu's feathers were magic and that arrows feathered with them could not miss their mark.

Skins and furs came from the deer, bear, bobcat and fox. These kept the people warm. Robes made of rabbit fur were used for sleeping blankets. Much food was provided by the deer and other animals

Tupi's people lived with the animals and knew their ways. They took what they needed for food, but all was used and none was wasted. They knew the meaning of conservation.

THE SEASONS

A-wa-ni's falls were friendly now, and Tupi watched the mist drifting gently through the tall trees. But in the spring, when melting snows flooded the streams, the falls made the earth tremble with their fury. Later in the summer when all of the snow was gone from the great mountains many of the waterfalls would become dry. Tupi liked best the Indian summer, when the black oaks became golden and shed their acorns.

Finally, as winter approached, the Indian families would prepare to leave their valley and go to the foothills. Sometimes some of them stayed but deep snow covered the ground and it was cold.

Although the waterfalls were beautiful to look at the Indians feared them. They believed that to be touched by the winds blowing from them would bring bad luck, for they were the breaths of evil spirits.

Slowly, Tupi filled his water basket and turned toward the village.

THE ARROW-MAKER

In front of his cedar bark uma-cha sat Tupi's grandfather, The Arrow-maker. In his left hand he held a piece of shiny black rock, while with his right hand he chipped it with a tool made from the antler of the deer. Patiently he worked, until the arrow point was sharp and to his liking. The good black rock came from the country of the Mo-no, across the great mountains. Each summer Tupi's people made the long journey to trade acorns and baskets for salt, pine nuts, and the arrow-rock, called "obsidian".

Taking a shaft made from the sweet-scented shrub the old man carefully fitted the finished point to it, gluing it with pitch and wrapping it tightly with string from the skin of the deer.

Tupi watched as his grandfather fastened feathers of Lee-ka to the end of the arrow, to give it flight as swift and as straight as that of the hawk.

When he had finished, the old man laid the arrow aside and smiled at the boy. He had given Tupi his name, and from him Tupi had learned the legends of his people, the Mi-woks, and how the A-wa-ni, their deep grassy valley, was made. These stories were part of Tupi's schooling, and now he was hoping that his grandfather would tell him more about the Coyote-man, who the Indians believed had made the moon and the stars, and the world and all of the people.

COYOTE-MAN

★ ★

Leaning back against the bark of his house, the old man began his story:

In the beginning Coyote-man made the world. Taking Frog-man with him he set out on a raft. When they reached a certain place Coyote-man told Frog-man to dive down and bring up some earth. From this, Coyote-man made the land. Then came others to live there—Lizard-man, Cougar-man, Star-woman, Fish-man, Grizzly Bear-woman, Fox-man, and more.

Coyote-man then told Lizard-man and the others that they must all turn into animals, and they took the forms which they have to this day. Next Coyote-man went all over the land and at each place where he wanted people to live he placed two feathers in the ground—one from the buzzard and one from the crow. Then he turned the feathers into men and women. They built villages and became strong. They worshipped the Great Spirit and the sun which kept them warm, and they were happy.

While Tupi's grandfather was talking other boys of the village had silently gathered around him. They wanted to hear the tale, for The Arrow-maker was the best story-teller of all. When the grandfather had finished not a word was spoken. The boys looked from one to another. Coyote-man was magic.

THE HOOP AND POLE GAME

Suddenly one of the boys gave a shout, waving a hoop in the air. Eager to play, all raced to the big meadow for the hoop and pole game.

Tupi brought the round hoop made of wood. It was about a foot across, covered with buckskin. Quickly he rolled the hoop toward the others. One by one they threw their slender poles at the rolling hoop, trying to throw them through the ring. When a boy missed, he went to the end of the line. Tupi liked to play this game, and it taught him to make his eyes and muscles work together. The boys who played it well grew up to be good hunters, Tupi knew.

THE HUNTERS RETURN

★ ★

A call from the canyon wall brought the game to a sudden end. The hunters were returning! They had left early in the morning to climb the cliffs near Cho-lok, the great falls, to search for Hi-ka, the deer. Some wore deer antlers on their heads and deer skins over their bodies to attract the deer.

Excitedly the boys ran up the trail toward the cliff. Soon through the trees the noisy group appeared, the hunters followed by chattering boys, and the boys followed by barking dogs. The hunt had been a good one, and there would be deer meat at the feast.

The men of the village began to skin the deer, using knives made from sharpened leg bones of the deer, for Tupi's people had no metal. The skins were taken off carefully. They would be tanned and made into summer clothing. All parts of the deer were used. Soon fires were heating rocks for earth ovens and children became more excited as feast time drew near.

FOOD FROM ACORNS

★ ★

The Great Spirit had been kind and the black oaks had many acorns the autumn before. Tupi had spent many days helping his mother and his grandmother gather them. Acorns were stored for the coming year in chuk-kas, which looked like haystacks of pine needles set on high poles.

Now was the time for giving thanks to the Great Spirit and this was why all of the village was making preparations for the feast. Tupi's grandmother sat on a huge flat stone. In the stone were many shallow holes and it was in one of these that she was grinding acorns for making Indian bread. Tupi watched her sway backward and forward as she lifted the heavy pounding rock again and again. Now and then she paused to scrape the bits of acorn into a mound. When all had been pounded into fine meal and placed in a basket, Tupi helped his grandmother carry it to the edge of the river, where the sand was smooth. Here they made a shallow hole in the sand. Into this the old lady carefully placed some of the acorn meal, levelling and patting the top with her hand. Now began the important work of removing the bitterness from the meal, using water from the river.

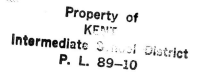

Tupi had been heating round, smooth stones in a fire which his father had made beside the river. With a bent stick he lifted the warm stones from the fire and dropped them into a large basket filled with water. As the water became warm the grandmother dipped some of it out in a small basket and poured it carefully over the acorn meal in the sand. She held a small branch of the incense-cedar tree beneath the basket as she poured so the warm water would go evenly over the acorn flour and not make a hole in it. Ten times she poured the warm water and allowed it to soak through, until all of the bitterness had been washed away. Now it was ready to eat—as soup, or thick mush, or baked into **cakes**.

THE LEGEND OF TU-TOK-A-NULA

While they worked, Tupi coaxed his grandmother to tell him the story of the measuring worm, Tu-tok-a-nula, and how he saved the little Indian children. She had told him the legend more times than she could remember, but she was always glad to tell it again.

Once upon a time, long ago, two little Indian boys went swimming in the river which flows through the valley called A-wa-ni. When they tired of swimming they climbed up on a warm rock on the bank and went to sleep. While they slept the rock began to grow. It grew and grew until its top was in the clouds and the little Indians touched their noses against the moon. And still they slumbered on. Finally the children awoke, and seeing how far it was down to the valley, they began to cry. Feeling sorry for them, the animals tried to get them down. First the white-footed mouse and then the wood rat tried but they could only jump a short distance up the smooth rock. Next came the coyote, who went higher, then the grizzly bear, who gave a great leap but fell back. Finally the mighty lion tried, jumping farther than any of the others, but he also failed. When all had tried and failed, the little measuring worm, Tu-tok-a-nula, began to inch his way up the cliff. For many sleeps he climbed until at last he reached the top. Taking the little Indian boys on his back he made his way carefully down. By staying with his task the measuring worm succeeded where the great animals failed. In his honor the Indians named the great rock after him.[1]

[1] It is known today as El Capitan.

THE FEAST

Tupi's eyes widened—never had he seen such a feast! The deer meat was ready to come out of the ovens; rabbits were roasting over the coals, and fish from the river. There were mounds of golden acorn bread and baskets of sweet bulbs and elderberries. A special treat was ka-cha-vee, insects tasting like shrimp, which came from Mo-no Lake, across the great mountains.

Everyone was seated on the ground. There was much story-telling and the canyon walls echoed with their laughter. Tupi ate and ate until he could eat no more.

NIGHT

The feast was over and Tupi lay back on his bed of furs. A tree frog sang his croaking song to a chorus of crickets. In the sky thousands of stars shone down upon him. And from the fireside came the murmur of voices as the men of the village talked of the hunt. They spoke of those who had been the most brave and they spoke of those who were the best marksmen. Tupi shut his eyes and thought about the day when he would go with his father on the hunt. He would be the bravest of them all and he would shoot the largest deer. His mother and father would be proud. His grandmother and grandfather would be proud. But just as a great feast was being prepared in his honor, Tupi fell asleep.

A*uthor's Note*: Speaking in 1877 of the legend of Tu-tok-a-nula, Stephen Powers (in Heiser and Whipple's *The California Indians*, Berkeley, 1951) said: "This is not only a true Indian story, but it has a pretty meaning, being a kind of parallel to the fable of the hare and the tortoise that ran a race. What the great animals of the forest could not do the despised measuring worm accomplished simply by patience and perseverance. It also has its value as showing the Indian idea of the formation of Yosemite . . ." Phonetic spelling of many Indian names is after Powers.

Other references consulted in the preparation of this booklet included Barrett and Gifford, *Miwok Material Culture*, Milwaukee, 1933, and Godfrey, "Yosemite Indians", a special issue of *Yosemite Nature Notes*, Yosemite National Park, 1941. The story of Coyote men is from Wilson, *The Lore and the Lure of Yosemite*, San Francisco, 1925, and from Barrett, *Myths of the Southern Sierra Miwok*, Berkeley, 1919. Indian animal names are from the latter source. Illustrations were made by Mr. Vella from Miwok artifacts in the Yosemite Museum.

To the many teachers who made suggestions and helpful criticism, our grateful thanks.

CROWN PRINTING & LITHOGRAPHING CO.
FRESNO, CALIFORNIA